This is a photograph of the River Tay.
This charming stretch of water begins its life in the Highlands of Perthshire, near the picturesque village of Killin. From there, it tumbles down towards the sea, passing such places as Dunkeld and Perth, before widening into an estuary at the city of Dundee. In the foreground are Roger Kettle (writer) and Andrew Christine (artist).

I HAVE GREAT PLANS FOR THIS YEAR.

4108

A CHAIN OF CLASSY FAST-FOOD RESTAURANTS.

"BUCKETS-O'-MINCE"!

THESE RESTAURANTS OF MINE WILL BE REALLY CLASSY.

4109

CANDLES ON THE TABLES?

GOOD IDEA!

"Have Tables."

ROBINSON CRUSOE CALLED HIS NEW FRIEND "FRIDAY."

HE NAMED HIM AFTER THE DAY HE MET HIM.

WHAT'S HIS SECOND NAME— "HALF PAST TWO"?

A LONELY MAN IN A DESOLATE LANDSCAPE,

ROBINSON CRUSOE AND I HAVE A LOT IN COMMON,

HE WAS FAT, WAS HE?

DENNIS, ROBINSON CRUSOE IS A CLASSIC.

A TALE OF ONE MAN'S BATTLE TO SURVIVE IN A HOSTILE ENVIRONMENT,

SO, TO ANSWER YOUR QUESTION— NO, THERE'S NO SNOGGING IN IT.

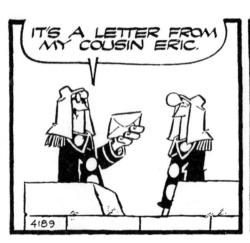

AMERICA—THAT'S THE PLACE I SHOULD BE!

THEY RESPECT PEOPLE LIKE ME WITH AN OPEN ATTITUDE TOWARDS MONEY.

Dear Mr. President of America, send me lots of dollars.

4221

Dear Mr. President of America,

I've seen pictures of you on the lawn outside your famous home...

...the little white house on the prairie.

4222

Dear Mr. President of America,

I believe you have an expression in your country about "Worshipping the Dollar."

You're a busy man—bung some in the post and I'll worship them for you.

4223

Dear Mr. President of America,

Your country has given the world so many wonderful things.

Though I could've done without Jimmy Osmond.

Being President of America, You must be very clever.

You must have to deal with many tricky questions.

What does "A-wop-bop-a-loo-bop-a-lop-bam-boom" mean?

A REPLY FROM THE PRESIDENT OF AMERICA!

"THE PRESIDENT THANKS YOU FOR YOUR FASCINATING LETTER..."

"...BUT REGRETS HE COULDN'T GIVE YOU DOLLY PARTON'S PHONE NUMBER."

PEEP IN THE
DAILY STAR
BRITAIN'S BRIGHTEST NEWSPAPER

I'VE BEEN THINKING OF A NAME FOR MY NEW RESTAURANT.

I WANTED SOMETHING CLASSY AND FRENCH-SOUNDING.

SO WHAT'S IT TO BE?

"MONSIEUR MINCE."

I'D REALLY LIKE TO OWN A CLASSY RESTAURANT.

CATER ONLY FOR A SOPHISTICATED CLIENTELE.

THE TYPE WHO KNOW WHICH SPOON TO USE WITH MINCE.

SIGH! OWNING A RESTAURANT OF MY OWN!

IT'S THE ONE DREAM I HAVE!

WELL, APART FROM THE ONE ABOUT DORIS DAY AND THE CUSTARD.